MW01070754

this journal belongs to

_____

Hi Pretty Humans!

My name is Rachel, and I am so glad you have invested in your Inner Child!

When I first started doing Inner Child work, I didn't think it would do much to heal my decade-long patterns of self-betrayal, enmeshment, and obsessive attachment.

I was certain that my eating disorder, anxiety, depression, low self-worth, and constant insecurity about love were solvable with medication and weekly therapy. But after 10+ years in therapy and countless trials with medication, I was still stuck in the same cyclical patterns.

Inner Child healing pulled me out of these patterns, embracing me with a warm and sensational courage that fueled a sense of relief I had never encountered.

In 2019, I started working with a therapist who introduced me to the concept of our Inner Child. Despite having been in therapy for over a decade *and* attending graduate school to get my own education in mental health counseling, I was hesitant.

I was already resistant to exercises like affirmations and self-compassion: the thought of talking to myself with so much kindness felt painfully uncomfortable and ridiculous.

I knew that many of the approaches I tended to cringe or shy away from ended up being the most productive, so I trusted her and leaned into the process.

In our sessions, my therapist had me start connecting to my Inner Child. We tapped into old wounds around worth, safety, belonging, and autonomy. These sessions hit so viscerally that I could sense how deeply those wounds were hidden.

This work was transformative. In a matter of months, I had discovered truths about my eating disorder, depression, anxiety, and self-worth that I had never tapped into during years of therapy and study. My healing practice was no longer about building bandaids for the wounds I kept re-opening: it was about honoring these wounds as real parts of my past, and reclaiming pride and acceptance for the scars I now bear.

What I have learned since doing Inner Child work is that my cyclical patterns, relationship tumbles and scrapes, and reactions to my failures or setbacks are entrenched in wounds sustained in childhood. They are not representations of my brokenness or disease. They are reasonable adaptations to making sense of what it means to be in and of this world.

I no longer shame or ridicule myself for failure or setback. I no longer live in a constant state of self-deprication or self-hatred. I have learned to re-teach my Inner Child the skills and wisdom from my adult self how she deserves to be in the world.

This is the very act and practice of healing our Inner Child.

Inner Child Healing is a reckoning with the ways our childhood selves adapted to the adult world with the best tools they had, and loving them enough to show them new ways.

It is my hope that you too will meet this reckoning in the pages of this journal.

Welcome to the next chapter in your life.

XO,

Rachel Havekost

how to use this journal

Each day will consist of specific prompts.

The prompts are recycled daily, and I have mixed and matched the categories for you.

No two days will be the same.

My own practice is daily (with lots of permission for days off if I'm just not up for it). I like to journal first thing in the morning with my cup of coffee, as it helps me shift my mood state into the direction I desire, and supports me in feeling grounded and stable for the rest of my day.

No matter what, give yourself grace and permission to not be perfect. I intentionally did not have the days in this journal align with specific dates, because if you miss a day, I don't want you to see an empty page in your journal or feel shame for missing a day. It's ok. You're human. You are doing the best you can, and I love you for it!

It is up to you when you start, and to trust your intuition to tell you how often to practice. There is no law or regulation on how often you are meant to journal: this is your practice, nobody else's.

Since this journal is focused on discovering, healing, and re-parenting your Inner Child, I invite you to tap into your wise Inner Parent as much as you can when answering the prompts. (Don't worry, I'll tell you more about how to do that in the pages to come!)

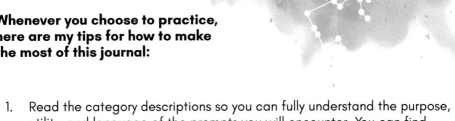

Whenever you choose to practice, here are my tips for how to make the most of this journal:

1. Read the category descriptions so you can fully understand the purpose, utility, and language of the prompts you will encounter. You can find instructions for each journaling category on on page 21.

2. Refer to page 19 and familiarize yourself with the Needs Wheel. You'll be using this for several daily prompts.

3. Create a "Ritual Space." I highly recommend creating a ritual space—a spot in your home, a time of day, and using the 5 senses to create a full, experiential "space" that becomes your journaling time and spot. My ritual space includes a cozy spot wherever I am (I travel full-time so it's not always the same), takes place first thing in the morning, and is accompanied with soft music, the warmth and smell of my coffee, and a pretty candle if I have access to one.

4. Turn off your phone or other notifications, and ask anyone you live with not to bother you while you write in your journal. The more uninterrupted this experience, the deeper flow you will come in contact with, and the richer the experience will be.

5. If you struggle with any of the prompts, I invite you to practice self-compassion. Be kind to yourself. It's ok if some of these don't come naturally—that's why it's a practice! It's something to return to, to try again, and to learn and grow from. This is not a test, competition, or task—it is simply a practice.

   Let's begin.

why inner child work?

We are so deeply connected in ways we cannot see or conceptualize to those who came before us, and their life experience lives on through us.

Many historically significant psychologists and their theories are—for lack of better word—old. Not old in age or presentation, but old in that their perspectives and theories were born decades ago, and much has changed since then.

We are born into this world and the first touch we receive is how we know what it means to be safe or unsafe.

Newer research and ideas indicate it is much more than our caregiver's parenting style that influences our ability to develop into emotionally and psychologically functioning humans. We have to look to history, systems, and culture to help us paint a bigger picture for the broad lens we put on developmental psychology.

I say all of this because it is vitally important as you do your Inner Child work to acknowledge that your parents did the best they could. Our work now is to heal these wounds so that we stop this cycle.

Doing this work is an act of rebellion to the systems that tell us we are meant to push ourselves to the limit. It is a giant F*** you to a culture of shame. Do this work for yourself first. And then do it so that you can make waves of defiance in a capitalist society where rest, play, and community have been shoved deep into the background.

This is Inner Child work.

what is my inner child?

Our Inner Child is the true "me" that has an intuitive knowing about themselves and the world. They are curious, creative, and interested in the world. When we tap into our Inner Child, we open ourselves up to re-learning what it means to be safe, loved, and supported.

The Inner Child is an archetype of our adolescent self. It is a representation of the part of ourselves that either flourished and grew in a developmentally supportive environment, or adapted to environments that were unsupportive or harmful.

The Thriving Inner Child

When our Inner Child is "wound-free," we are able to move about our life as adults relatively well. We engage securely with ourselves and others.

We feel safe often, and are able to recognize danger and evaluate risks appropriately. We are confident in our abilities and generally like who we are. We feel capable to try new things, are curious, and express delight in experimentation. Failure does not change how we feel about ourselves, and we feel good about our ability to learn from mistakes. Play, joy, and freedom are accessible. We don't judge others regularly, and we celebrate the success of our peers.

These are signs that in childhood our needs were met—or that we have developed a wise Inner Parent to support our Inner Child when they feel threatened, triggered, or afraid.

the wounded inner child

From birth, we come into this world like a sponge. We absorb most of the information about ourselves, the world, and what it means to be a human from our caregivers. They are our primary library of love, support, and safety. Before our internal structures are emotionally, cognitively, and physiologically mature, we are at the utter whim of the connections and observations we have with the adults who are meant to protect us.

There are several theories of childhood development, but all of them have one common theme: If in childhood our needs are not met, we will sustain some type of "wound."

At each developmental phase of childhood, hopefully our caregivers can provide us with the quality of attention, love, and support we need in order to learn that we are safe, free, good, and capable.

Our core needs in childhood include:

Safety/Security
Belonging/Connection
Dependency/Nourishment
Independence/Freedom
Agency/Autonomy
Vulnerability and Selfhood
Worth/Equality

When our core needs are not met by our caregivers, we adopt wounded beliefs around these needs. Some of these beliefs include:

I am unsafe
I am unwanted
I don't matter
I have no power
I don't have needs
I'm on my own
I am incapable
I am too much
I am not enough
I am misunderstood
I don't belong anywhere
I am unlovable
I am unworthy

These wounds follow us into adulthood, where we fall into cycles of self-betrayal, overexertion, angry outbursts, withdrawal, isolation, saying too much, saying too little, overstepping boundaries, having no privacy, isolating, fearing love, fearing ourselves, denying our realities, and falling into a self-abusive, draining existence.

How do we sustain inner child wounds?

If, in childhood, our core, developmental needs were not met, we adapt in the best ways we know how. Without the developmental, cognitive, social, or emotional maturity of an adult with lived experiences, it is difficult for us to know as kiddos how to meet these needs on our own.

Inner child wounds are sustained when:

- Our core needs are not met by our caregivers
- Our intuition or creativity is stifled, denied, or criticized
- We aren't told we are loved, special, or accepted
- Our caregivers overly specialize or deify us
- Our caregivers send mixed or conflicting messages about love
- We are abused, used, or manipulated by our parents for their own unmet childhood needs
- We aren't taught boundaries, or our boundaries are violated
- Our cries for support or help are denied or called "neediness"
- We aren't taught emotion regulation or healthy emotion expression
- Our parents don't mirror us at a young age
- We aren't given permission to explore, experiment, or take risks
- We are responsible for doing everything alone, or even caretaking our own parents
- Independence is discouraged and problems/decisions are solved/ made for us

Inner Child wounds are not just about singular moments of trauma or abrasion, though they can stem from traumatic events. These wounds are about ongoing attempts to learn how to exist in the world, when, as vulnerable adolescents, the people and systems we relied on didn't have the ideal tools to teach us.

A Note On Intergenerational Trauma:

Ideal environments, parenting styles, and developmental accomplishments at each stage of childhood are based in theories and research of psychologists like Jean Piaget, Ron Kurtz, Erik Erikson, Mary Ainsworth, John Bowlby, Albert Bandura, Lawrence Kohlberg, Carl Jung, Vygotsky, Abraham Maslow, Karen Horney, and more.

We now must acknowledge the ways in which not only our nuclear family, but our wider communities impacted us as young children. These networks impacted our caregivers, and vicariously impacted how they raised us. We cannot ignore how national and global history have influenced those systems, and how our governing bodies and culture have been the puppeteers of it all. The web of these systems cannot be overlooked as a source of influence that traces centuries back, and threads directly to the present day influencing us all.

I still believe our primary relationship with our caregivers is of the utmost importance: we are tethered to them through DNA. We are born into this world and the first touch we receive is how we know what it means to be safe or unsafe. These intimate relationships between child and parent are the life force that brings us here.

Our parents sustained their own Inner Child wounds, whether through lack of care and nurturance from their parents, or from systemic oppression and culture of shame. We cannot overlook abuse, trauma, and historical trauma as sources of wounds in our lineage: even if we cannot point to a specific instance in our immediate family, it is likely that trauma lives somewhere in our ancestral constellation.

By engaging in Inner Child work, we are not just placing a bandaid on our wounds so that we can live freely in our own life. We engage with this work so that we can pass down the most loving, nurturing, and productive form of care we can harness to the generations to come.

We are biologically primed for connection. For community. For love and support. For safety. These needs run deep, and we have lost them. Now is the time to reclaim them, and to learn ways to provide for our own love and security so that we in turn can reach out and teach it to others. This is how we can learn what it means to connect with others on a rich, meaningful, and safe level.

Signs Our Inner Child is Wounded

We sustain Inner Child wounds when one or more of our childhood needs are denied, oppressed, undervalued, shamed, or criticized.

Sometimes we sustain these wounds because our caregivers are unavailable (physically or emotionally). Other times it is because our caregivers are inconsistent in their parenting, either in their individual approach or in their separate opposing approaches.

If the people in our nuclear families and communities have their own complex mode of dealing with stress, shame, fear, or conflict, we as kiddos will either mirror their behaviors, reject them and develop counter behaviors, or bounce back and forth between the two.

We move through adolescence picking up on the cues around us, absorbing the information like a sponge to help us understand how to make sense of ourselves and the world. As we grow, these behaviors solidify and take form, giving us the impression that they "are the way it is" and that our way of being is unchangeable.

These adaptations show up in adulthood in our relationships, and can sometimes leave us wondering if, in fact, we've gotten it all wrong.

Here are some signs in our adult lives that we may have Inner Child wounds to tend to:

Signs in Relationships

- Codependency (relying heavily on another person to soothe, heal, or fix us)
- Under-dependency (belief of "I don't need anyone or anything")
- Prioritizing self over others to the point of lacking community or relationships
- Fantasizing about being "chosen" or saved by a romantic partner
- Fantasizing about saving or rescuing a romantic partner
- Do-it-myself attitude/I don't need help from anyone
- Trouble with setting boundaries, sticking to boundaries, and saying no
- People-pleasing or self-betraying our own needs in order to prevent feared abandonment
- Changing personality, interests, values, or appearance to mold to a romantic interest "chameleon-like"
- Difficulty trusting others/Difficulty trusting self
- Trouble asking for support or help
- Judging others harshly or seeing certain behaviors as right/wrong, good/bad

Signs in Cognition and Thinking

- Difficulty making decisions or problem-solving without reassurance or help
- Second-guessing, self-doubting, or lacking intuition
- Trouble completing tasks or finishing projects
- Setting unrealistic or perfectionistic expectations for ourselves (often so great we cannot achieve them)
- Trouble focusing in the present moment, mind-racing, easily distracted
- Difficulty recalling memories, both from childhood and adulthood
- Signs in Self-Perception and Emotion
- Low self-worth, self-esteem, and self-confidence
- Intense emptiness, anxiety, and panic when losing a relationship
- Using food, material items, alcohol, drugs, or sex to soothe feelings of emptiness or loneliness
- Belief you are incapable/unable to do things on your own
- Lack of creativity, curiosity, or interest in exploring/trying new things
- Inability/difficulty regulating intense emotions
- Fear of emotional expression (it won't end once I start)
- Difficulty expressing emotions/believe emotional world is burdensome

*While this is an extensive list, it is not exhaustive. Nor is it diagnostic. These characteristics show up for almost all humans at some point in life: we are not perfect, nor are we meant to be. These are merely meant to function as clues that perhaps we have some reflection to do, and we can see these signs as opportunities to tend to our Inner Child so that we can thrive and flourish individually and collectively.

what is the wise inner parent?

The Inner Parent is an archetype of our wisest self: the part of us that intuitively knows we are worthy, whole, and good. It is an extension of who we are that allows us to re-parent our Inner Child, both in exercises like this journal, and in moments when our Inner Child is triggered.

Our wise Inner Parent is compassionate, understanding, and supportive. They are able to witness the Inner Child part of ourselves without judgment or shame. Our wise Inner Parent is able to strike a balance of holding space and love while offering guidance and wisdom. It is, in essence, a part of ourselves that knows intuitively what we need when life gets a little shaky.

By developing a strong sense of our wise Inner Parent, we cultivate space between an event and our reactions. A seasoned wise Inner Parent can quickly identify when our Inner Child is triggered, and is able to soothe, support, or coach them.

In this delicate separation of selves, we actually learn to become more conscious, aware, and integrated. We learn to take a step back from our experiences and witness them with wisdom, intuition, and knowing.

To develop our wise Inner Parent, we begin by identifying what our Inner Child lacked in adolescence. Our wise Inner Parent can then step in to fill the gaps in learning, support, or care that were missing, using tools, exercises, and lessons learned in the pages of this journal.

In this journal, you will engage in exercises that ask you to call on your wise Inner Parent: you may be asked to write from the perspective of them, or to imagine what they might say to help you navigate a journaling prompt.

Here are some things to keep in mind to help you access your wise Inner Parent:

- What do you wish a caregiver had said or done in your childhood?
- What tone of voice or facial expression do you find comforting or soothing?
- If you had a child, how would you speak to them to let them know you loved them?
- How would you let your own child know they were safe?
- What words do you wish a caregiver had used to describe you?
- What kind of physical contact would you have liked to receive/not receive from a caregiver?
- What lessons, skills, or tools do you wish your caregiver had taught you?
- How could your caregiver have expressed trust and support if you wanted to try something on your own?

Cultivating a wise Inner Parent is a practice. It is an ongoing learning experience, and no matter how you do it is right, because it is intended to be your wise Inner Parent. For you, and you alone.

if you get stuck...

Here are some suggestions!

- Ask yourself what a friend or partner might say.

- Skip the prompt and return to it at the end of the practice.

- Think about what I (Rachel) might respond with.

- Leave it blank. This is for YOU—not for me, not for your mom or dad, not for anyone else. If something isn't resonating, say, "welp, that shit's not for me today!" and move on!

faq's

I have some questions, Rach!

How long does each journal take?
Each entry takes about 5-10 minutes—that's it! Sometimes it takes me less time, sometimes more—it all depends on the prompts, your mood, and how focused you feel that day.

Is it ok to do it at different times of the day?
I find that doing it at the same time of day creates a habit, which makes it more likely that you'll continue to do it on a a daily, ritual basis. Doing it in the morning sets me up for the rest of the day—by the time it's afternoon I've already missed out on several hours where the inner parenting, needs assessment, or affirmations could have come in handy. This is why I recommend folks use it in the morning, but again it's your practice, so do it when it feels best for you!

This sounds like a lot of work. is it hard?
It is hard starting out—as someone who struggles deeply with self-criticism, anxiety, depression, and low self-esteem, these are all activities that stir up resistance, judgment, and doubt. That's ok! I invite you to become aware of it feeling challenging, and use that as information. What is the resistance saying? Does this feel hard because it's new, or because I'm simply not in the headspace today? All of it is valid and true, and I invite you to take your time moving through this journal.

Where are all these categories from?
I was a student of therapy (as in I was IN therapy and I also went to graduate school to become a therapist) for over a decade, and these are a collection of tools I learned over the years. The tools are drawn from and inspired by Attachment Theory, Zen Mindfulness, Dialectical Behavior Therapy, Cognitive Behavioral Therapy, Rational Emotive Behavior Therapy, Rogerian and Adlerian psychodynamic models, body psychology, the Hakomi Institute's character typing, Neurolinguistic reprogramming, Reiki, Jungian archetypes, Existential theory, and more.

What if I can't think of something for the prompt?
That's ok! I invite you to be super kind to yourself if (and when) this happens. I still struggle sometimes to answer certain prompts, even if they are prompts I see all the time. Our brains get tired, we have off days, and life is simply not linear.

needs wheel

Use this needs wheel to identify your needs.

Start by asking yourself:
"What do I need in this moment?"

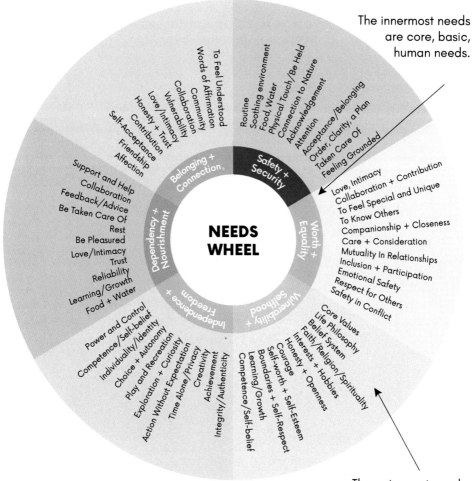

The innermost needs are core, basic, human needs.

The outermost needs are specific, actionable, tangible needs.

You can start by indentifying a core need and tracing it out to something more specific, or start on the outside and discover the core need underlying it!

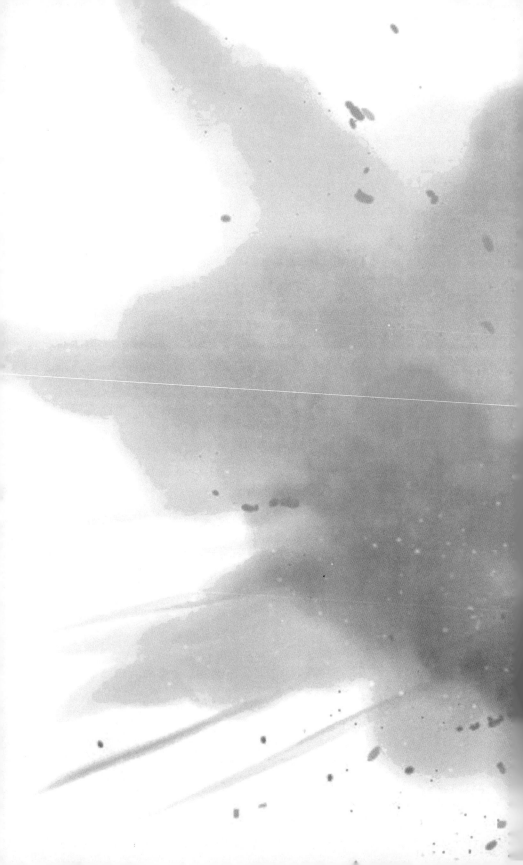

journaling categories

On the next several pages you'll find descriptions for each journaling category and instructions for using the prompts in your journaling templates.

01   **mindfulness**

02   **needs**

03   **affirmations**

04   **letters to your inner child**

05   **inner parent & inner child dialogues**

01 mindfulness

Mindfulness is the art of painting without plan. Singing without lyrics. Observing without changing. Mindfulness opens our minds to the possibility that there is no right or wrong way to do, be, think, or feel: everything just "is."

Mindfulness can be a daunting practice for many people--I know it was for me. The idea of slowing down, focusing on one thing in the moment, and simply noticing (rather than evaluating) what I was doing seemed nonsensical.

I needed to understand why mindfulness could possibly impact me positively, otherwise I wouldn't practice it. I didn't understand how a few minutes of focusing on an object could have much benefit in my daily life.

Mindfulness grounds us in the present moment: it forces our minds to stay with what is here and now, and encourages us to connect with our bodies, instead of shut ourselves off to them. This is a critical re-learning process if we've experienced any trauma, as trauma can cause us to disconnect from our bodies, dissociate, or find ways to mentally escape from the present moment.

In the context of Inner Child healing, mindfulness reconnects us with our sense of curiosity, wonder, and play. I learned over the years that mindfulness, when used daily, can drastically improve our ability to free ourselves from judgment, let go of attachments, and allow life to just "be."

Many of the exercises in this journal come from Zen Mindfulness, which is the act of non-judgmental awareness. By connecting to your senses, noticing what's in your surroundings, and accepting your thoughts and feelings non-judgmentally, you learn to witness the world as an unbiased observer: as a child in wonder.

While practicing Mindfulness, I invite you to keep the following in mind:

- There is no right or wrong way to practice mindfulness. Practice freeing yourself from "how" the task is done, or whether it is correct. However you do it is the right way. *This is the art of non-attachment: we release our expectations of how something is "intended" to turn out.* By allowing space for any and all outcomes, we learn to reduce anxiety, anticipation, or disappointment in our lives. We become more flexible and able to adapt to uncertainty and change.

- If you notice your thoughts trailing away from the exercise, or if you become distracted, simply notice it, and return your mind back to the task at hand.

- In mindfulness, "judgments" are used to describe all adjectives or descriptions of an experience or object—not just negative evaluations. The goal in mindfulness is to let go of all judgments, both positive and negative. In doing so, we allow ourselves to see things just as they are, without any evaluation. Notice any "judgments" that arise as you practice mindfulness, observing them and slowly letting them float away.

Rachel's tip*: Try using "beginner's mind," meaning you treat the activity as if you were a newborn baby, engaging with the task for the very first time.*

affirmations

Affirmations are medicine statements about oneself or the way we see the world. They are designed to harness new beliefs or solidify shaky ones. Affirmations are true or what one hopes to be true.

Affirmations are not just tools for amplifying self-worth. Yes, affirmation-writing is one of the most powerful ways to shift ourselves out of feeling worthless and into a state of confidence. And, affirmations can be used to affirm all kinds of beliefs, including those we hold about our environments, communities, and relationships.

In the context of Inner Child healing, you will be using affirmations to help reinforce or enforce beliefs that are specific to the developmental tasks of childhood. You will create healing statements, which with repetition have the power to re-wire old beliefs surrounding core wounds.

With regular practice, affirmations can become the most pivotal tool in your Inner Child healing practice.

When doing affirmations, I invite you to keep the following in mind:

- Affirm qualities about yourself, rather than possessions or accolades. (i.e. "I have a really cool bicycle" is not an affirmation that will help you build self-worth/esteem. It might make your bike feel really good, which is nice, but this is for you.)

- Make affirmations that you are working towards, for example, if you wish you were more confident, make an affirmation like, "I am working every day on building my confidence."

- Make affirmations that you might not fully believe now, but want to. Even if you don't believe it now, you can still make the affirmation, "I am a confident person," and eventually, you'll believe it.

- Try making affirmations about how you see the world, as much as about how you see yourself. For example, you can make an affirmation like "The world is a safe place for me to explore."

Rachel's tip: There is no right way to do this! It's ok if it feels hard or sticky at first. This is why it is a practice: it is not a test, and you are finding your way through all of it.

03 needs

Our needs are different from our wants in that they serve to keep us alive, nourished, and connected. They are, in many ways, the bare minimum of what it means to be a human. When we become more attuned to our own unique needs, we learn to be in the world authentically and thrive interpersonally.

As a young adult, I had absolutely no idea what I needed. What do I need? No one had ever asked me that before. I assumed that my lack of knowing meant I simply didn't have needs: I must not need much of anything, and even if I did need something, I certainly wasn't going to ask anyone to help me.

This narrative kept me safe in many ways: it protected me from potential heartbreak, disappointment, and rejection. But it also kept me locked away from any real connection, and it put stark walls between me and those I hoped to be in relationship with.

In this journal, you will see prompts asking you to identify your daily needs. Refer to page 19 to see the "Needs Wheel" to help you identify your needs. Once you've identified your needs, you'll be asked to list anything you can do to get those needs met. This could include activities, mantras, reaching out for support, or planning.

When practicing writing your needs, I invite you to keep the following in mind:

- Needs are not selfish. Needs are human requirements for life, thriving, and flourishing. If you notice yourself thinking "this is ridiculous, I don't actually need this," simply notice that thought and ask yourself "how has not acknowledging this need hurt me?"

- If you get stuck on identifying a need, ask yourself "what might someone else say in this scenario?"

- When writing your needs, pay close attention to times when you judge, criticize, or shame your needs. Where does this voice come from? Whose voice is it? What would it mean in your life to let go of this voice? Can you give yourself permission to let go of that voice, just for this moment as you write down these needs?

Rachel's tip: *This practice is also about re-learning that it is safe and ok to have needs! You may find it useful to write a mantra in these sections about it being OK to have the needs you've identified.*

letters to your inner child

Letters you write to your Inner Child from the perspective of your present self or Inner Parent. These are small tokens of self-compassion, wisdom, hope, and guidance that we can access using this magnificent healing tool.

Writing a letter to yourself is a powerful way to step outside your daily thought structures. It offers you a set of fresh lenses through which to see yourself, and ultimately, treat yourself. It is also an effective way to set yourself up for challenging days, as you can look back on these letters long after you've written them.

In this journal, you will be asked to write letters to your Inner Child, from the perspective of your wise Inner Parent. This means you will be channeling the wisdom and compassion of your Inner Parent, and harnessing their language, words, and perspective as a healing modality.

These letters serve two purposes:

- They may heal old wounds, allowing us to hear the words we wished we had heard our caregivers say as children.

- They cultivate our strength as a wise Inner Parent, and exercise these muscles so that when our Inner Child is triggered in daily life, we have experience speaking as our Inner Parent to our Inner Child.

When writing letters to yourself, I invite you to keep the following in mind:

- What tone of voice would you use if you were attempting to be compassionate?

- What language or words would you use if you were trying to be wise?

- How can you be understanding and compassionate, but still offer wisdom and knowing?

Rachel's tip: *Let your pen flow. No one else is reading this but you, and it is for nobody else but you.*

05 inner child & inner parent dialogues

Written dialogue between your Inner Child and Inner Parent to support you in stating the needs of your Inner Child, then meeting those needs from the voice of your wise Inner Parent.

This exercise will offer you the chance to have a back and forth dialogue between your Inner Child and Inner Parent.

Each prompt will focus on a certain time period in childhood. At each of these stages of life we encounter different developmental tasks:

Infancy (0-2 years old): During this stage, our primary task is to know that we are safe, wanted, and that we belong. This is our first introduction into the world, and hopefully we learn that we can trust the people who are caring for us to meet our basic needs and care for us. *Hopefully, we learn that we are safe and have the right to exist.*

Toddler (2-5 years old): During this stage, our primary task is to experiment with what it means to be separate from our caregivers. We begin to say "no," assert our likes and dislikes, and try things on our own. Still, we look back to our caregivers for support when we aren't sure of ourselves, and begin the delicate balance of being self-sufficient and still being dependent on our caregiver. *Hopefully we learn we can have needs and get those needs met, whether independently or dependently.*

School Age (5-11 years old): During this stage, our primary task is to develop a social sense of self and grow more deeply into our independence. We start setting boundaries, assessing values, and exploring the world that exists outside of our nuclear family system. *Hopefully we learn we have freedom and the right to be ourselves.*

Teen (12-18 years old) During this stage, our primary task is to deepen our identity and place in the world. We size ourselves up socially, and hopefully we funnel those comparisons into celebration and acceptance over jealousy or loss of confidence. *Hopefully, we learn that we are worthy and have the right to be equal.*

These dialogues will assist you in tapping into each of these unique phases, and ask you to write to your wise Inner Parent from the perspective of each of these childhood stages. What will come from this is a discovery of specific unmet needs, which will assist your wise Inner Parent in knowing how to best support your Inner Child as a whole.

When writing the Inner Child and Inner Parent dialogues, I invite you to keep the following in mind:

- This practice may be the one where you experience the most resistance. You may notice your Inner Critic pop up, who may say things like "this is dumb" or "how am I supposed to do this?" Jot down the words of your Inner Critic in the corners of your journal and witness them from the perspective of your Inner Parent. Whose voice is that? Where did it come from? How can you use your Inner Parent to help you navigate this voice?

- If you notice resistance to a certain time period, I invite you to become curious. Why might there be resistance to this particular age? What happened during this time? Why do I avoid it? Allow resistance to be a clue of its own into your self-discovery.

- If you struggle to remember specifics during any time period, that's ok! I suggest trying to think about feelings, sensations, or even making guesses instead of concrete memories. Before we develop language, our memories are stored "implicitly," meaning in our unconscious. These memories are not stored as pictures or stories with words and events: we store them as sensations or a general feeling/knowing. When we are stressed or living in survival mode, our brains bypass storing memories "explicitly," so we can sometimes only have implicit memories even from parts of childhood when we do have language.

Rachel's tip: If the prompt itself doesn't resonate that day, skip to a different day! If something doesn't resonate, it's likely that your intuition is steering you elsewhere in the journal. Follow it.

90 days
of journaling

before you begin this transformation...

take a moment to reflect

Setting intentions is a wonderful way to begin a new practice with clarity, alignment, and commitment. Before beginning on this adventure, take a moment to reflect on why you are here.

What are your intentions for this journal? Why is this practice important to you, and what do you hope to gain?

example journal entry

today's date: <u>December 1st, 2020</u>

Mindfulness: *One thing in the moment.* Find an object nearby and imagine you are seeing it for the first time as a child. Write down your observations below.

I observed my coffee mug. I noticed I got distracted a lot. I tried to say "that's interesting" when I did and return to the mug. I noticed it's shape and color. it seemed smooth. I saw a crack in one part. the handle was a different color than the rest.

Needs: Using the Needs Wheel on page 19 identify what you need today. Then make a list of what you can do to get those needs met today.

I need to feel free to really express myself. I need to find some creative outlet where I can really "let it all out." I need to dance or move my body in some way, because I think this will help me feel that sense of expression and almost like a full body HERE I AM or something. I need to be able to be silly and goofy, so I guess I need to surround myself with people who appreciate that part of my personality.

Affirmations: *Dependence.* Affirm ways you can depend on others for support or help.

1. It's ok for me to ask for support.

2. If someone offers to help me with someone, it doesn't take away from my ability to do it alone.

3. When I lean on others for support, I build trust and vulnerability in my relationships.

---

checklist

It's time to get started! Before beginning, make sure you've completed each item below so you can get the most out of this journal.

- [ ] I've read the descriptions of Inner Child, Inner Parent, and about Inner Child wounds.

- [ ] I've read through each category description.

- [ ] I've written down my intentions on page 29 and how I'm feeling at the start of this journey.

- [ ] I promise to give this journal my best effort, and release any expectations of the outcome.

- [ ] I've reviewed the example journal on the left.

- [ ] I love myself no matter how this goes, and will always love myself no matter what!

day 01

*"Caring for myself is not self-indulgence, it is
self-preservation, and that is an act of political warfare."*
-Audre Lorde

today's date: _____

Mindfulness: *Non Dominant Drawing.* Using your non-dominant hand, free draw in the space below. You can do this for as little or as long as you like.

Needs: Using the Needs Wheel on page 19 identify what you need today. Then make a list of what you can do to get those needs met today.

Affirmations: *Safety.* Affirm ways in which you are safe: this is in regards to trusting yourself and others, feeling safe in your body, and being safe right here and now.

1.

2.

3.

day 02

"Live as if you were living a second time, and as though you had acted wrongly the first time."
-Viktor Frankl

today's date: _____

Mindfulness: *Free Drawing.* Set a timer for one minute. Doodle in the space provided. If your thoughts wander or if you notice yourself starting to make judgments about your doodling, simply notice those thoughts and return your attention to your drawing.

Needs: Using the Needs Wheel on page 19 identify what you need today. Then make a list of what you can do to get those needs met today.

Affirmations: *Security.* Affirm your sense of security: feeling secure in who you are, what you enjoy, or what you believe.

1.

2.

3.

day 03

"Accept yourself; then others will."

today's date: _____

Mindfulness: *Body Scan.* Imagine you are a toddler learning about your body parts for the first time. Starting with your feet, touch each part of your body gently and safely, name the body part and notice what it feels like to really connect physically and mentally to each area.

Needs: Using the Needs Wheel on page 19 identify what you need today. Then make a list of what you can do to get those needs met today.

Affirmations: *Belonging.* Affirm the ways you belong: how you belong on this earth, this universe, in your social world, and to yourself.

1.

2.

3.

day 04

"What is coming is better than what is gone."
–Arabic Proverb

today's date: _____

Letter to Your Inner Child: *You Matter.* From the perspective of your Wise Inner Parent, write your Inner Child a letter about why they matter.

day 05

"If you surrendered to the air, you could ride it."
-Toni Morrison

today's date: _____

Mindfulness: *Spaghetti / Robot.* Sit in a comfortable position with your legs and arms uncrossed, or lay down flat on your bed or the ground. Tense every muscle in your body like you have become a stiff robot, including your face, hands, toes, all of it! Then, release everything, imagining you are like spaghetti flopping on the ground. Repeat this 4-5 times, holding the "robot" and "spaghetti" for 5 seconds at a time.

Needs: Using the Needs Wheel on page 19 identify what you need today. Then make a list of what you can do to get those needs met today.

Affirmations: *Worth.* Affirm your worth: your inherent worth, your worthiness of love, and being enough.

1.

2.

3.

day 06

"To fall in love with yourself is the first secret to happiness."
-Robert Morely

today's date: _____

Mindfulness: *Connect the Dots.* Starting from the left of the box below, connect the dots from left to right without lifting your pen from the page. You can connect all or just some of the dots, it's up to you!

· ·
· ·
· ·
· ·

Needs: Using the Needs Wheel on page 19 identify what you need today. Then make a list of what you can do to get those needs met today.

Affirmations: *Value.* Affirm your value: how you bring value to others, that you matter, and what is valuable about who you are.

1.

2.

3.

day 07

"Expectations are resentments waiting to happen."
-Brene Brown

today's date: _____

Mindfulness: *One thing in the moment.* Find an object nearby and imagine you are seeing it for the first time as a child. Write down your observations below.

Needs: Using the Needs Wheel on page 19 identify what you need today. Then make a list of what you can do to get those needs met today.

Affirmations: *Dependence.* Affirm ways you can depend on others for support or help.

1.

2.

3.

day 08

"The greater your storm the brighter your rainbow."

today's date: _____

Inner Child Inner Parent Dialogue: *Infancy.* As an infant, we don't yet have words to express our emotions. If you could imagine yourself having words as a baby, what would you say to your parents? What might you ask for? Write a brief dialogue between your Inner Infant and your Inner Parent from this perspective.

day 09

*"You yourself, as much as anybody in the entire universe,
deserve your love and affection."*
–Buddha

today's date: _____

Mindfulness: *Little Pleasures.* Find an object in your home that sparks joy. Set a timer for one minute, and simply observe this object. You can use all your senses: smell, touch, sight, sound. If thoughts or distractions arise, simply notice them and let them float away. Write down what this experience was like below.

Needs: Using the Needs Wheel on page 19 identify what you need today. Then make a list of what you can do to get those needs met today.

Affirmations: *Vulnerability.* Affirm your pride or sense of vulnerability in life instead of shame or criticism.

1.

2.

3.

day 10

"Worrying won't stop bad stuff from happening. It just keeps you from enjoying the good."

today's date: _____

Mindfulness: *Object Naming.* Set a timer for one minute. Look all around you, and in your mind, list everything you see. Try to remain non-judgmental, meaning not adding any qualitative words to the objects you see. After the minute is up, jot down what the experience was like for you in the space below.

Needs: Using the Needs Wheel on page 19 identify what you need today. Then make a list of what you can do to get those needs met today.

Affirmations: *Love.* Affirm your lovability and ability to love.

1.

2.

3.

day 11

"It's okay if you fall apart sometimes. Tacos fall apart and we still love them."

today's date: _____

Mindfulness: *One thing in the moment.* Find an object nearby and imagine you are seeing it for the first time as a child. Write down your observations below.

Needs: Using the Needs Wheel on page 19 identify what you need today. Then make a list of what you can do to get those needs met today.

Affirmations: *Uniqueness.* Affirm the ways you are special and unique.

1.

2.

3.

day 12

"Great things never came from comfort zones."

Letter to Your Inner Child: *I'm Proud of You.* From the perspective of your Wise Inner Parent, write your Inner Child a letter telling them you are proud of them and why.

day 13

*"Caring for your inner child has a powerful and surprisingly
quick result: Do it and the child heals."*
–Martha Beck

today's date: _____

Mindfulness: *Non-Attachment.* Find something in your space that you can observe for a minute. As you observe it, allow the thought "nothing is permanent" to arise. As it does, notice what other thoughts pop up, without any judgment. Notice how your perception of the object changes over the course of the minute. Jot down your experience below.

Needs: Using the Needs Wheel on page 19 identify what you need today. Then make a list of what you can do to get those needs met today.

Affirmations: *Equality.* Affirm your equality: that you are just as good as others, that you celebrate others, and that we are all equal.

1.

2.

3.

day 14

"I'm finding my feet in the mud."
-Faith Score

today's date: _____

Mindfulness: *Little Pleasures*. Find an object in your home that sparks joy. It can be an old photo, a childhood token, something fuzzy, anything that makes you smile or brings joy. Set a timer for one minute, and simply observe this object. You can use all your senses: smell, touch, sight, sound. If thoughts or distractions arise, simply notice them and let them float away. Write down what this experience was like below.

Needs: Using the Needs Wheel on page 19 identify what you need today. Then make a list of what you can do to get those needs met today.

Affirmations: *Safety*. Affirm ways in which you are safe: this is in regards to trusting yourself and others, feeling safe in your body, and being safe right here and now.

1.

2.

3.

day 15

"Remember you were once a toddler who strutted with her belly forward."

today's date: _____

Mindfulness: *Free Doodle.* Set a timer for one minute. Doodle in the space provided. If your thoughts wander or if you notice yourself starting to make judgments about your doodling, simply notice those thoughts and return your attention to your drawing.

Needs: Using the Needs Wheel on page 19 identify what you need today. Then make a list of what you can do to get those needs met today.

Affirmations: *Security.* Affirm your sense of security: feeling secure in who you are, what you enjoy, or what you believe.

1.

2.

3.

day 16

"Seek to be whole, not perfect."
-Oprah

today's date: _____

Inner Child Inner Parent Dialogue: *Toddler*. As toddlers, we start to discover our sense of freedom, independence and power. Think of yourself between the ages of 2-5. What might you have wanted to say to your parents. What did you need to hear from them about trying new things, making mistakes, and boundaries? Write a brief dialogue between your Inner Toddler and your Inner Parent from this perspective.

day 17

"The way to walk in freedom is to surrender control."

today's date: _____

Mindfulness: *Non Dominant Drawing*. Using your non-dominant hand, free draw in the space below. You can do this for as little or as long as you like.

Needs: Using the Needs Wheel on page 19 identify what you need today. Then make a list of what you can do to get those needs met today.

Affirmations: *Belonging*. Affirm the ways you belong: how you belong on this earth, this universe, in your social world, and to yourself.

1.

2.

3.

---

day 18

"Sometimes, it's not the times you decide to fight, but the times you decide to surrender that make all the difference."
–Sissy Gavrilaki

today's date: _____

Mindfulness: *Free Drawing.* Set a timer for one minute. Doodle in the space provided. If your thoughts wander or if you notice yourself starting to make judgments about your doodling, simply notice those thoughts and return your attention to your drawing.

Needs: Using the Needs Wheel on page 19 identify what you need today. Then make a list of what you can do to get those needs met today.

Affirmations: *Worth.* Affirm your worth: your inherent worth, your worthiness of love, and being enough.

1.

2.

3.

day 19

"Don't feel guilty doing what is best for you."
-Hannah Neese

today's date: _____

Mindfulness: *Body Scan.* Imagine you are a toddler learning about your body parts for the first time. Starting with your feet, touch each part of your body gently and safely, name the body part and notice what it feels like to really connect physically and mentally to each area.

Needs: Using the Needs Wheel on page 19 identify what you need today. Then make a list of what you can do to get those needs met today.

Affirmations: *Value.* Affirm your value: how you bring value to others, that you matter, and what is valuable about who you are.

1.

2.

3.

day 20

"The most sophisticated people I know—
inside they are all children."
–Jim Hensen

today's date: _____

Letter to Your Inner Child: *Unconditional Love.* From the perspective of your Wise Inner Parent, write your Inner Child a letter telling them you are proud of them and why.

day 21

*"If something goes wrong in your life, just yell, plot twist!
And move on."*

today's date: _____

Mindfulness: *Spaghetti / Robot.* Sit in a comfortable position with your legs and arms uncrossed, or lay down flat on your bed or the ground. Tense every muscle in your body like you have become a stiff robot, including your face, hands, toes, all of it! Then, release everything, imagining you are like spaghetti flopping on the ground. Repeat this 4-5 times, holding the "robot" and "spaghetti" for 5 seconds at a time.

Needs: Using the Needs Wheel on page 19 identify what you need today. Then make a list of what you can do to get those needs met today.

Affirmations: *Dependence.* Affirm ways you can depend on others for support or help.

1.

2.

3.

day 22

"To pay attention, this is our endless and proper work."
–Mary Oliver

today's date: _____

Mindfulness: *Connect the Dots.* Starting from the left of the box below, connect the dots from left to right without lifting your pen from the page. You can connect all or just some of the dots, it's up to you!

· ·
· ·
· ·
· ·

Needs: Using the Needs Wheel on page 19 identify what you need today. Then make a list of what you can do to get those needs met today.

Affirmations: *Vulnerability.* Affirm your pride or sense of vulnerability in life instead of shame or criticism.

1.

2.

3.

day 23

"All water has a perfect memory and is forever trying to get back to where it was."
-Toni Morrison

today's date: _____

Mindfulness: *One Thing in the Moment*. Find an object nearby and imagine you are seeing it for the first time as a child. Write down your observations below.

Needs: Using the Needs Wheel on page 19 identify what you need today. Then make a list of what you can do to get those needs met today.

Affirmations: *Love*. Affirm your lovability and ability to love.

1.

2.

3.

day 24

"Flowers need time to bloom. So do you."
-Sajid Al Sayed

today's date: _____

Inner Child Inner Parent Dialogue: *School Age.* Between the ages of 5-11, we start to develop a social sense of self. We begin to witness ourselves as unique individuals, as well as begin to asses how our values and family values are different than those of our friends. We develop boundaries and assert ourselves. What would you have liked to say to your caregiver from this age view? What would you have liked to say to your caregiver as you entered the social world and learned about life outside your nuclear family? Write a brief dialogue between your Inner School Age Child and your Inner Parent from this perspective.

day 25

"Doubt kills more dreams than failure ever will."
-Suzy Kassem

today's date: _____

Mindfulness: *Little Pleasures.* Find an object in your home that sparks joy. Set a timer for one minute, and simply observe this object. You can use all your senses: smell, touch, sight, sound. If thoughts or distractions arise, simply notice them and let them float away. Write down what this experience was like below.

Needs: Using the Needs Wheel on page 19 identify what you need today. Then make a list of what you can do to get those needs met today.

Affirmations: *Uniqueness.* Affirm the ways you are special and unique.

1.

2.

3.

day 26

"One day you will tell your story of how you overcame what you went through and it will be someone else's survival guide."
-Brene Brown

today's date: _____

Mindfulness: *Object Naming.* Set a timer for one minute. Look all around you, and in your mind, list everything you see. Try to remain non-judgmental, meaning not adding any qualitative words to the objects you see. After the minute is up, jot down what the experience was like for you in the space below.

Needs: Using the Needs Wheel on page 19 identify what you need today. Then make a list of what you can do to get those needs met today.

Affirmations: *Equality.* Affirm your equality: that you are just as good as others, that you celebrate others, and that we are all equal.

1.

2.

3.

day 27

"The more you let go, the higher you rise."
-Yasmin Mogahed

today's date: _____

Mindfulness: *One Thing in the Moment.* Find an object nearby and imagine you are seeing it for the first time as a child. Write down your observations below.

Needs: Using the Needs Wheel on page 19 identify what you need today. Then make a list of what you can do to get those needs met today.

Affirmations: *Safety.* Affirm ways in which you are safe: this is in regards to trusting yourself and others, feeling safe in your body, and being safe right here and now.

1.

2.

3.

day 28

"Trust the timing of your life."
–Brittany Burgunder

today's date: _____

Letter to Your Inner Child: *I Want You.* From the perspective of your Wise Inner Parent, write your Inner Child a letter about how they are wanted.

day 29

*"When we are no longer able to change a situation, we
are challenged to change ourselves."*
-Viktor Frankl

today's date: _____

Mindfulness: *Non-Attachment.* Find something in your space that you can observe for a minute. As you observe it, allow the thought "nothing is permanent" to arise. As it does, notice what other thoughts pop up, without any judgment. Notice how your perception of the object changes over the course of the minute. Jot down your experience below.

Needs: Using the Needs Wheel on page 19 identify what you need today. Then make a list of what you can do to get those needs met today.

Affirmations: *Belonging.* Affirm the ways you belong: how you belong on this earth, this universe, in your social world, and to yourself.

1.

2.

3.

day 30

"Don't compare your life to others. There's no comparison between the sun and the moon, they shine when it's their time."
-Stephanie H. Brown

today's date: _____

Mindfulness: *Little Pleasures.* Find an object in your home that sparks joy. It can be an old photo, a childhood token, something fuzzy, anything that makes you smile or brings joy. Set a timer for one minute, and simply observe this object. You can use all your senses: smell, touch, sight, sound. If thoughts or distractions arise, simply notice them and let them float away. Write down what this experience was like below.

Needs: Using the Needs Wheel on page 19 identify what you need today. Then make a list of what you can do to get those needs met today.

Affirmations: *Equality.* Affirm your equality: that you are just as good as others, that you celebrate others, and that we are all equal.

1.

2.

3.

you've journaled for 30 days!

take a moment to reflect

Reflection is one of the biggest indicators of future success. It allows us to see where we started, how we've grown, and teaches our brains that we are adaptable and flexible beings.

In the space below, free-write about the last month. What did you learn? What was challenging? How have you grown? What would you like to tell yourself as the next 30 days unfold?

day 31

"A mind is like a parachute. It doesn't work if it isn't open."
-Frank Zappa

today's date: _____

Mindfulness: *One Thing in the Moment.* Find an object nearby and imagine you are seeing it for the first time as a child. Write down your observations below.

Needs: Using the Needs Wheel on page 19 identify what you need today. Then make a list of what you can do to get those needs met today.

Affirmations: *Worth.* Affirm your worth: your inherent worth, your worthiness of love, and being enough.

1.

2.

3.

day 32

"I exist as I am, that is enough."
-Walt Whitman

today's date: _____

Inner Child Inner Parent Dialogue: *Teen Years.* Between the ages of 12-18, we start to test the boundaries of our identity, and experiment with what it means to be an equal member of society. We start to wrestle with ideas of worth, likability, and acceptance as we come into our sense of self. From this age what would you have liked to say to your caregiver? What would you have liked to hear from them? Write a brief dialogue between your Inner Teen and your Inner Parent from this perspective.

day 33

"Honor your inner child by losing yourself in simple pleasures."
-Kim Del Valle Walker

Mindfulness: *Non Dominant Drawing.* Using your non-dominant hand, free draw in the space below. You can do this for as little or as long as you like.

Needs: Using the Needs Wheel on page 19 identify what you need today. Then make a list of what you can do to get those needs met today.

Affirmations: *Dependence.* Affirm ways you can depend on others for support or help.

1.

2.

3.

day 34

"Be yourself. Everyone else is already taken."
-Oscar Wilde

today's date: _____

Mindfulness: *Free Drawing.* Set a timer for one minute. Doodle in the space provided. If your thoughts wander or if you notice yourself starting to make judgments about your doodling, simply notice those thoughts and return your attention to your drawing.

Needs: Using the Needs Wheel on page 19 identify what you need today. Then make a list of what you can do to get those needs met today.

Affirmations: *Uniqueness.* Affirm the ways you are special and unique.

1.

2.

3.

day 35

"Be brave enough to be bad at something new."
–Jon Acuff

today's date: _____

Mindfulness: *Body Scan.* Imagine you are a toddler learning about your body parts for the first time. Starting with your feet, touch each part of your body gently and safely, name the body part and notice what it feels like to really connect physically and mentally to each area.

Needs: Using the Needs Wheel on page 19 identify what you need today. Then make a list of what you can do to get those needs met today.

Affirmations: *Vulnerability.* Affirm your pride or sense of vulnerability in life instead of shame or criticism.

1.

2.

3.

day 36

"When joy is a habit, love is a reflex."
-Bob Goff

today's date: _____

Letter to Your Inner Child: *Autonomy.* From the perspective of your Wise Inner Parent, write your Inner Child a letter letting them know they are free.

day 37

"Being positive in a negative situation is not naive.
It's leadership."
-Ralph Marston

today's date: _____

Mindfulness: *Spaghetti / Robot.* Sit in a comfortable position with your legs and arms uncrossed, or lay down flat on your bed or the ground. Tense every muscle in your body like you have become a stiff robot, including your face, hands, toes, all of it! Then, release everything, imagining you are like spaghetti flopping on the ground. Repeat this 4-5 times, holding the "robot" and "spaghetti" for 5 seconds at a time.

Needs: Using the Needs Wheel on page 19 identify what you need today. Then make a list of what you can do to get those needs met today.

Affirmations: *Uniqueness.* Affirm the ways you are special and unique.

1.

2.

3.

day 38

"Authenticity is the daily practice of letting go of who we think we're supposed to be and embracing who we are."
-Brene Brown

today's date: _____

Mindfulness: *Connect the Dots.* Starting from the left of the box below, connect the dots from left to right without lifting your pen from the page. You can connect all or just some of the dots, it's up to you!

· ·
· ·
· ·
· ·

Needs: Using the Needs Wheel on page 19 identify what you need today. Then make a list of what you can do to get those needs met today.

Affirmations: *Dependence.* Affirm ways you can depend on others for support or help.

1.

2.

3.

---

day 39

"You are the artist of your own life. Don't hand the paintbrush to anyone else."
-Iva Ursano

today's date: _____

Mindfulness: *One Thing in the Moment.* Find an object nearby and imagine you are seeing it for the first time as a child. Write down your observations below.

Needs: Using the Needs Wheel on page 19 identify what you need today. Then make a list of what you can do to get those needs met today.

Affirmations: *Equality.* Affirm your equality: that you are just as good as others, that you celebrate others, and that we are all equal.

1.

2.

3.

day 40

"You have so much to offer as the person you are right now."
-Robyn Conley Downs

today's date: _____

Inner Child Inner Parent Dialogue: *Infancy.* As an infant, we don't yet have words to express our emotions. If you could imagine yourself having words as a baby, what would you say to your parents? What might you ask for? Write a brief dialogue between your Inner Infant and your Inner Parent from this perspective.

day 41

"I hope you live a life you're proud of. If you find that you are not, I hope you have the strength to start all over again."
-F. Scott Fitzgerald

today's date: _____

Mindfulness: *Little Pleasures.* Find an object in your home that sparks joy. Set a timer for one minute, and simply observe this object. You can use all your senses: smell, touch, sight, sound. If thoughts or distractions arise, simply notice them and let them float away. Write down what this experience was like below.

Needs: Using the Needs Wheel on page 19 identify what you need today. Then make a list of what you can do to get those needs met today.

Affirmations: *Security.* Affirm your sense of security: feeling secure in who you are, what you enjoy, or what you believe.

1.

2.

3.

day 42

"Feel what you need to feel and then let it go. Do not let it consume you."
-Dhiman

today's date: _____

Mindfulness: *Object Naming.* Set a timer for one minute. Look all around you, and in your mind, list everything you see. Try to remain non-judgmental, meaning not adding any qualitative words to the objects you see. After the minute is up, jot down what the experience was like for you in the space below.

Needs: Using the Needs Wheel on page 19 identify what you need today. Then make a list of what you can do to get those needs met today.

Affirmations: *Belonging.* Affirm the ways you belong: how you belong on this earth, this universe, in your social world, and to yourself.

1.

2.

3.

day 43

"You don't have to control your thoughts. You just have to stop letting them control you."
-Dan Millman

today's date: _____

Mindfulness: *One Thing in the Moment.* Find an object nearby and imagine you are seeing it for the first time as a child. Write down your observations below.

Needs: Using the Needs Wheel on page 19 identify what you need today. Then make a list of what you can do to get those needs met today.

Affirmations: *Worth.* Affirm your worth: your inherent worth, your worthiness of love, and being enough.

1.

2.

3.

day 44

"How you love yourself is how you teach others to love you."
–Rupi Kaur

today's date: _____

Letter to Your Inner Child: *I Will Protect You.* From the perspective of your Wise Inner Parent, write your Inner Child a letter about how you will protect them.

day 45

"Mindfulness: the intentional use of attention."
–Leah Weiss

today's date: _____

Mindfulness: *Non-Attachment.* Find something in your space that you can observe for a minute. As you observe it, allow the thought "nothing is permanent" to arise. As it does, notice what other thoughts pop up, without any judgment. Notice how your perception of the object changes over the course of the minute. Jot down your experience below.

Needs: Using the Needs Wheel on page 19 identify what you need today. Then make a list of what you can do to get those needs met today.

Affirmations: *Value.* Affirm your value: how you bring value to others, that you matter, and what is valuable about who you are.

1.

2.

3.

day 46

"Your future needs you. Your past doesn't."

today's date: _____

Mindfulness: *Little Pleasures.* Find an object in your home that sparks joy. It can be an old photo, a childhood token, something fuzzy, anything that makes you smile or brings joy. Set a timer for one minute, and simply observe this object. You can use all your senses: smell, touch, sight, sound. If thoughts or distractions arise, simply notice them and let them float away. Write down what this experience was like below.

Needs: Using the Needs Wheel on page 19 identify what you need today. Then make a list of what you can do to get those needs met today.

Affirmations: *Dependence.* Affirm ways you can depend on others for support or help.

1.

2.

3.

day 47

"Trust the wait. Embrace the uncertainty. Enjoy the beauty of becoming."

today's date: _____

Mindfulness: *Connect the Dots.* Starting from the left of the box below, connect the dots from left to right without lifting your pen from the page. You can connect all or just some of the dots, it's up to you!

· ·
· ·
· ·
· ·

Needs: Using the Needs Wheel on page 19 identify what you need today. Then make a list of what you can do to get those needs met today.

Affirmations: *Vulnerability.* Affirm your pride or sense of vulnerability in life instead of shame or criticism.

1.

2.

3.

day 48

"Bravery is the audacity to be unhindered by failures, and to walk with freedom, strength, and hope, in the face of things unknown."
–Morgan Harper Nichols

today's date: _____

Inner Child Inner Parent Dialogue: *Toddler.* As toddlers, we start to discover our sense of freedom, independence and power. Think of yourself between the ages of 2-5. What might you have wanted to say to your parents. What did you need to hear from them about trying new things, making mistakes, and boundaries? Write a brief dialogue between your Inner Toddler and your Inner Parent from this perspective.

day 49

"Ask for what you want and be prepared to get it."
-Maya Angelou

today's date: _____

Mindfulness: *Non Dominant Drawing.* Using your non-dominant hand, free draw in the space below. You can do this for as little or as long as you like.

Needs: Using the Needs Wheel on page 19 identify what you need today. Then make a list of what you can do to get those needs met today.

Affirmations: *Love.* Affirm your lovability and ability to love.

1.

2.

3.

day 50

"We don't stop playing because we grow old;
we grow old because we stop playing."
-George Bernard Shaw

today's date: _____

Mindfulness: *Free Drawing.* Set a timer for one minute. Doodle in the space provided. If your thoughts wander or if you notice yourself starting to make judgments about your doodling, simply notice those thoughts and return your attention to your drawing.

Needs: Using the Needs Wheel on page 19 identify what you need today. Then make a list of what you can do to get those needs met today.

Affirmations: *Uniqueness.* Affirm the ways you are special and unique.

1.

2.

3.

day 51

"You carry so much love in your heart.
Give some to yourself."

today's date: _____

Mindfulness: *Body Scan.* Imagine you are a toddler learning about your body parts for the first time. Starting with your feet, touch each part of your body gently and safely, name the body part and notice what it feels like to really connect physically and mentally to each area.

Needs: Using the Needs Wheel on page 19 identify what you need today. Then make a list of what you can do to get those needs met today.

Affirmations: *Equality.* Affirm your equality: that you are just as good as others, that you celebrate others, and that we are all equal.

1.

2.

3.

day 52

"It's ok. You just forgot who you are. Welcome back."

today's date: _____

Letter to Your Inner Child: *Trust.* From the perspective of your Wise Inner Parent, write your Inner Child a letter about how you trust them.

day 53

"If you feel like you're losing everything, remember that trees lose their leaves every year and still they stand tall and wait for better days to come."

today's date: _____

Mindfulness: *Spaghetti / Robot.* Sit in a comfortable position with your legs and arms uncrossed, or lay down flat on your bed or the ground. Tense every muscle in your body like you have become a stiff robot, including your face, hands, toes, all of it! Then, release everything, imagining you are like spaghetti flopping on the ground. Repeat this 4-5 times, holding the "robot" and "spaghetti" for 5 seconds at a time.

Needs: Using the Needs Wheel on page 19 identify what you need today. Then make a list of what you can do to get those needs met today.

Affirmations: *Safety.* Affirm ways in which you are safe: this is in regards to trusting yourself and others, feeling safe in your body, and being safe right here and now.

1.

2.

3.

---

day 54

You change the world by being yourself."
-Yoko Ono

today's date: _____

Mindfulness: *Connect the Dots.* Starting from the left of the box below, connect the dots from left to right without lifting your pen from the page. You can connect all or just some of the dots, it's up to you!

· ·

· ·

· ·

· ·

Needs: Using the Needs Wheel on page 19 identify what you need today. Then make a list of what you can do to get those needs met today.

Affirmations: *Security.* Affirm your sense of security: feeling secure in who you are, what you enjoy, or what you believe.

1.

2.

3.

day 55

*"Rock bottom will teach you lessons that mountain
tops never will."*
-Michelle Hannah Ministries

today's date: _____

Mindfulness: *One Thing in the Moment.* Find an object nearby and imagine you are seeing it for the first time as a child. Write down your observations below.

Needs: Using the Needs Wheel on page 19 identify what you need today. Then make a list of what you can do to get those needs met today.

Affirmations: *Belonging.* Affirm the ways you belong: how you belong on this earth, this universe, in your social world, and to yourself.

1.

2.

3.

day 56

"The wound is the place where the light enters you."
-Rumi

today's date: _____

Inner Child Inner Parent Dialogue: *School Age.* Between the ages of 5-11, we start to develop a social sense of self. We begin to witness ourselves as unique individuals, as well as begin to asses how our values and family values are different than those of our friends. We develop boundaries and assert ourselves. What would you have liked to say to your caregiver from this age view? What would you have liked to say to your caregiver as you entered the social world and learned about life outside your nuclear family? Write a brief dialogue between your Inner School Age Child and your Inner Parent from this perspective.

day 57

""Daring is saying I know I will eventually fail and I'm still all in."
-Brene Brown

today's date: _____

Mindfulness: *Little Pleasures.* Find an object in your home that sparks joy. Set a timer for one minute, and simply observe this object. You can use all your senses: smell, touch, sight, sound. If thoughts or distractions arise, simply notice them and let them float away. Write down what this experience was like below.

Needs: Using the Needs Wheel on page 19 identify what you need today. Then make a list of what you can do to get those needs met today.

Affirmations: *Worth.* Affirm your worth: your inherent worth, your worthiness of love, and being enough.

1.

2.

3.

day 58

"But even if I am weak, I can still be kind. For true power is in giving instead of taking."

today's date: _____

Mindfulness: *Object Naming.* Set a timer for one minute. Look all around you, and in your mind, list everything you see. Try to remain non-judgmental, meaning not adding any qualitative words to the objects you see. After the minute is up, jot down what the experience was like for you in the space below.

Needs: Using the Needs Wheel on page 19 identify what you need today. Then make a list of what you can do to get those needs met today.

Affirmations: *Value.* Affirm your value: how you bring value to others, that you matter, and what is valuable about who you are.

1.

2.

3.

day 59

"If you get tired, learn to rest, not to quit."
–Banksy

today's date: _____

Mindfulness: *One Thing in the Moment.* Find an object nearby and imagine you are seeing it for the first time as a child. Write down your observations below.

Needs: Using the Needs Wheel on page 19 identify what you need today. Then make a list of what you can do to get those needs met today.

Affirmations: *Dependence.* Affirm ways you can depend on others for support or help.

1.

2.

3.

day 60

"The only way to make sense out of change is to plunge into it,
move with it, and join the dance."
–Alan Watts

today's date: _____

Letter to Your Inner Child: *Worth.* From the perspective of your Wise Inner Parent, write your Inner Child a letter about their worth.

you've journaled for 60 days!

take a moment to reflect

Reflection is one of the biggest indicators of future success. It allows us to see where we started, how we've grown, and teaches our brains that we are adaptable and flexible beings.

In the space below, free-write about the last month. What did you learn? What was challenging? How have you grown? What would you like to tell yourself as the next 30 days unfold?

day 61

"The opposite of play is not work. It's depression."
-Brian Sutton-Smith

today's date: _____

Mindfulness: *Non-Attachment.* Find something in your space that you can observe for a minute. As you observe it, allow the thought "nothing is permanent" to arise. As it does, notice what other thoughts pop up, without any judgment. Notice how your perception of the object changes over the course of the minute. Jot down your experience below.

Needs: Using the Needs Wheel on page 19 identify what you need today. Then make a list of what you can do to get those needs met today.

Affirmations: *Vulnerability.* Affirm your pride or sense of vulnerability in life instead of shame or criticism.

1.

2.

3.

day 62

"When someone says you can't do it, do it twice, and take pictures."
-Tami Xiang

Mindfulness: *Little Pleasures.* Find an object in your home that sparks joy. It can be an old photo, a childhood token, something fuzzy, anything that makes you smile or brings joy. Set a timer for one minute, and simply observe this object. You can use all your senses: smell, touch, sight, sound. If thoughts or distractions arise, simply notice them and let them float away. Write down what this experience was like below.

Needs: Using the Needs Wheel on page 19 identify what you need today. Then make a list of what you can do to get those needs met today.

Affirmations: *Love.* Affirm your lovability and ability to love.

1.

2.

3.

day 63

"Your anxiety doesn't come from thinking about the future, but from wanting to control it."
-Kahlil Girban

today's date: _____

Mindfulness: *Object Naming.* Set a timer for one minute. Look all around you, and in your mind, list everything you see. Try to remain non-judgmental, meaning not adding any qualitative words to the objects you see. After the minute is up, jot down what the experience was like for you in the space below.

Needs: Using the Needs Wheel on page 19 identify what you need today. Then make a list of what you can do to get those needs met today.

Affirmations: *Uniqueness.* Affirm the ways you are special and unique.

1.

2.

3.

day 64

"The creation of something new is not accomplished by the intellect but by the play instinct." -Carl Jung

today's date: _____

Inner Child Inner Parent Dialogue: *Teen Years.* Between the ages of 12-18, we start to test the boundaries of our identity, and experiment with what it means to be an equal member of society. We start to wrestle with ideas of worth, likability, and acceptance as we come into our sense of self. From this age what would you have liked to say to your caregiver? What would you have liked to hear from them? Write a brief dialogue between your Inner Teen and your Inner Parent from this perspective.

day 65

"You are not a drop in the ocean. You are the entire ocean in a drop."
–Rumi

today's date: _____

Mindfulness: *Non Dominant Drawing.* Using your non-dominant hand, free draw in the space below. You can do this for as little or as long as you like.

Needs: Using the Needs Wheel on page 19 identify what you need today. Then make a list of what you can do to get those needs met today.

Affirmations: *Equality.* Affirm your equality: that you are just as good as others, that you celebrate others, and that we are all equal.

1.

2.

3.

day 66

"I don't want to end up simply having visited this world."
–Mary Oliver

today's date: _____

Mindfulness: *Free Drawing.* Set a timer for one minute. Doodle in the space provided. If your thoughts wander or if you notice yourself starting to make judgments about your doodling, simply notice those thoughts and return your attention to your drawing.

Needs: Using the Needs Wheel on page 19 identify what you need today. Then make a list of what you can do to get those needs met today.

Affirmations: *Safety.* Affirm ways in which you are safe: this is in regards to trusting yourself and others, feeling safe in your body, and being safe right here and now.

1.

2.

3.

day 67

"I am not what happened to me, I am what I choose to become."
-Carl Jung

today's date: _____

Mindfulness: *Body Scan.* Imagine you are a toddler learning about your body parts for the first time. Starting with your feet, touch each part of your body gently and safely, name the body part and notice what it feels like to really connect physically and mentally to each area.

Needs: Using the Needs Wheel on page 19 identify what you need today. Then make a list of what you can do to get those needs met today.

Affirmations: *Security.* Affirm your sense of security: feeling secure in who you are, what you enjoy, or what you believe.

1.

2.

3.

day 68

"Having compassion for yourself and your body comes from embracing your humanness."

today's date: _____

Letter to Your Inner Child: *Capable.* From the perspective of your Wise Inner Parent, write your Inner Child a letter about their abilities and capabilities.

day 69

"When you become comfortable with uncertainty, infinite possibilities open up in your life."
-Eckhart Tolle

today's date: _____

Mindfulness: *Spaghetti / Robot.* Sit in a comfortable position with your legs and arms uncrossed, or lay down flat on your bed or the ground. Tense every muscle in your body like you have become a stiff robot, including your face, hands, toes, all of it! Then, release everything, imagining you are like spaghetti flopping on the ground. Repeat this 4-5 times, holding the "robot" and "spaghetti" for 5 seconds at a time.

Needs: Using the Needs Wheel on page 19 identify what you need today. Then make a list of what you can do to get those needs met today.

Affirmations: *Belonging.* Affirm the ways you belong: how you belong on this earth, this universe, in your social world, and to yourself.

1.

2.

3.

day 70

"When things change inside you, things change around you."
–Mark Twain

today's date: _____

Mindfulness: *Connect the Dots.* Starting from the left of the box below, connect the dots from left to right without lifting your pen from the page. You can connect all or just some of the dots, it's up to you!

· ·
· ·
· ·
· ·

Needs: Using the Needs Wheel on page 19 identify what you need today. Then make a list of what you can do to get those needs met today.

Affirmations: *Worth.* Affirm your worth: your inherent worth, your worthiness of love, and being enough.

1.

2.

3.

day 71

*"Uncertainty is the only certainty there is, and knowing how to
live with insecurity is the only security."*
-John Allen Paulos

today's date: _____

Mindfulness: *One Thing in the Moment.* Find an object nearby and imagine you are seeing it for the first time as a child. Write down your observations below.

Needs: Using the Needs Wheel on page 19 identify what you need today. Then make a list of what you can do to get those needs met today.

Affirmations: *Value.* Affirm your value: how you bring value to others, that you matter, and what is valuable about who you are.

1.

2.

3.

day 72

"One moment can change a day, one day can change a life, and one life can change the world."
–Buddha

today's date: _____

Inner Child Inner Parent Dialogue: *Infancy.* As an infant, we don't yet have words to express our emotions. If you could imagine yourself having words as a baby, what would you say to your parents? What might you ask for? Write a brief dialogue between your Inner Infant and your Inner Parent from this perspective.

day 73

"No one can make you feel inferior without your consent."
-Eleanor Roosevelt

today's date: _____

Mindfulness: *Little Pleasures.* Find an object in your home that sparks joy. Set a timer for one minute, and simply observe this object. You can use all your senses: smell, touch, sight, sound. If thoughts or distractions arise, simply notice them and let them float away. Write down what this experience was like below.

Needs: Using the Needs Wheel on page 19 identify what you need today. Then make a list of what you can do to get those needs met today.

Affirmations: *Dependence.* Affirm ways you can depend on others for support or help.

1.

2.

3.

day 74

*"You are worth the quiet moment. You are worth the deeper breath.
You are worth the time it takes to slow down, be still, and rest."*
-Morgan Harper Nichols

today's date: _____

Mindfulness: *Object Naming.* Set a timer for one minute. Look all around you, and in your mind, list everything you see. Try to remain non-judgmental, meaning not adding any qualitative words to the objects you see. After the minute is up, jot down what the experience was like for you in the space below.

Needs: Using the Needs Wheel on page 19 identify what you need today. Then make a list of what you can do to get those needs met today.

Affirmations: *Vulnerability.* Affirm your pride or sense of vulnerability in life instead of shame or criticism.

1.

2.

3.

day 75

"Live life as if everything is rigged in your favor."
–Rumi

today's date: _____

Mindfulness: *One Thing in the Moment*. Find an object nearby and imagine you are seeing it for the first time as a child. Write down your observations below.

Needs: Using the Needs Wheel on page 19 identify what you need today. Then make a list of what you can do to get those needs met today.

Affirmations: *Love*. Affirm your lovability and ability to love.

1.

2.

3.

day 76

"If you don't live your life, then who will?"
–Rihanna

today's date: _____

Letter to Your Inner Child: *Seen + Understood*. From the perspective of your Wise Inner Parent, write your Inner Child a letter about how you understand them.

day 77

Your life isn't yours if you always care what someone else thinks."
-Jade Marie

today's date: _____

Mindfulness: *Non-Attachment.* Find something in your space that you can observe for a minute. As you observe it, allow the thought "nothing is permanent" to arise. As it does, notice what other thoughts pop up, without any judgment. Notice how your perception of the object changes over the course of the minute. Jot down your experience below.

Needs: Using the Needs Wheel on page 19 identify what you need today. Then make a list of what you can do to get those needs met today.

Affirmations: *Uniqueness.* Affirm the ways you are special and unique.

1.

2.

3.

day 78

"The soul usually knows what to do to heal itself. The challenge is to silence the mind."
–Caroline Myss

today's date: _____

Mindfulness: *Little Pleasures.* Find an object in your home that sparks joy. It can be an old photo, a childhood token, something fuzzy, anything that makes you smile or brings joy. Set a timer for one minute, and simply observe this object. You can use all your senses: smell, touch, sight, sound. If thoughts or distractions arise, simply notice them and let them float away. Write down what this experience was like below.

Needs: Using the Needs Wheel on page 19 identify what you need today. Then make a list of what you can do to get those needs met today.

Affirmations: *Equality.* Affirm your equality: that you are just as good as others, that you celebrate others, and that we are all equal.

1.

2.

3.

day 79

"Self-love is becoming home to yourself, the same home you are to others."
-Dhiman

today's date: _____

Mindfulness: *Spaghetti / Robot.* Sit in a comfortable position with your legs and arms uncrossed, or lay down flat on your bed or the ground. Tense every muscle in your body like you have become a stiff robot, including your face, hands, toes, all of it! Then, release everything, imagining you are like spaghetti flopping on the ground. Repeat this 4-5 times, holding the "robot" and "spaghetti" for 5 seconds at a time.

Needs: Using the Needs Wheel on page 19 identify what you need today. Then make a list of what you can do to get those needs met today.

Affirmations: *Safety.* Affirm ways in which you are safe: this is in regards to trusting yourself and others, feeling safe in your body, and being safe right here and now.

1.

2.

3.

day 80

*"You wanna fly, you got to give up the
shit that weighs you down"*
-Toni Morrison

today's date: _____

Inner Child Inner Parent Dialogue: *Toddler.* As toddlers, we start to discover our sense of freedom, independence and power. Think of yourself between the ages of 2-5. What might you have wanted to say to your parents. What did you need to hear from them about trying new things, making mistakes, and boundaries? Write a brief dialogue between your Inner Toddler and your Inner Parent from this perspective.

day 81

"Courage is the most important of all the virtues, because without courage you can't practice any other virtue consistently."
-Maya Angelou

today's date: _____

Mindfulness: *Non Dominant Drawing.* Using your non-dominant hand, free draw in the space below. You can do this for as little or as long as you like.

Needs: Using the Needs Wheel on page 19 identify what you need today. Then make a list of what you can do to get those needs met today.

Affirmations: *Security.* Affirm your sense of security: feeling secure in who you are, what you enjoy, or what you believe.

1.

2.

3.

day 82

"Play is the beginning of knowledge."
-George Dorsey

today's date: _____

Mindfulness: *Free Drawing.* Set a timer for one minute. Doodle in the space provided. If your thoughts wander or if you notice yourself starting to make judgments about your doodling, simply notice those thoughts and return your attention to your drawing.

Needs: Using the Needs Wheel on page 19 identify what you need today. Then make a list of what you can do to get those needs met today.

Affirmations: *Belonging.* Affirm the ways you belong: how you belong on this earth, this universe, in your social world, and to yourself.

1.

2.

3.

day 83

"When I dare to be powerful - to use my strength in the service of my vision, then it becomes less and less important whether I am afraid."
-Audre Lorde

today's date: _____

Mindfulness: *Body Scan.* Imagine you are a toddler learning about your body parts for the first time. Starting with your feet, touch each part of your body gently and safely, name the body part and notice what it feels like to really connect physically and mentally to each area.

Needs: Using the Needs Wheel on page 19 identify what you need today. Then make a list of what you can do to get those needs met today.

Affirmations: *Worth.* Affirm your worth: your inherent worth, your worthiness of love, and being enough.

1.

2.

3.

day 84

"If you want to be creative, stay in part a child, with the creativity and invention that characterizes children before they are deformed by adult society."
-Jean Piaget

today's date: _____

Letter to Your Inner Child: *I'm Proud of You.* From the perspective of your Wise Inner Parent, write your Inner Child a letter telling them you are proud of them and why.

day 87

"Everything has changed and yet, I am more me than I've ever been."
-Iain Thomas

today's date: _____

Mindfulness: *One Thing in the Moment.* Find an object nearby and imagine you are seeing it for the first time as a child. Write down your observations below.

Needs: Using the Needs Wheel on page 19 identify what you need today. Then make a list of what you can do to get those needs met today.

Affirmations: *Vulnerability.* Affirm your pride or sense of vulnerability in life instead of shame or criticism.

1.

2.

3.

day 88

"Necessity may be the mother of invention, but play is certainly the father."
-Roger von Oech

today's date: _____

Inner Child Inner Parent Dialogue: *School Age.* Between the ages of 5-11, we start to develop a social sense of self. We begin to witness ourselves as unique individuals, as well as begin to asses how our values and family values are different than those of our friends. We develop boundaries and assert ourselves. What would you have liked to say to your caregiver from this age view? What would you have liked to say to your caregiver as you entered the social world and learned about life outside your nuclear family? Write a brief dialogue between your Inner School Age Child and your Inner Parent from this perspective.

day 89

"Letting go is an active process."
-Alicia Menendez

today's date: _____

Mindfulness: *Little Pleasures*. Find an object in your home that sparks joy. Set a timer for one minute, and simply observe this object. You can use all your senses: smell, touch, sight, sound. If thoughts or distractions arise, simply notice them and let them float away. Write down what this experience was like below.

Needs: Using the Needs Wheel on page 19 identify what you need today. Then make a list of what you can do to get those needs met today.

Affirmations: *Love*. Affirm your lovability and ability to love.

1.

2.

3.

day 90

*"Be messy and complicated and
afraid and show up anyway."*
-Glennon Doyle

today's date: _____

Mindfulness: *Non Dominant Drawing.* Using your non-dominant hand, free draw in the space below. You can do this for as little or as long as you like.

Needs: Using the Needs Wheel on page 19 identify what you need today. Then make a list of what you can do to get those needs met today.

Affirmations: *Uniqueness.* Affirm the ways you are special and unique.

1.

2.

3.

congratulations, gorgeous.

you've completed your 90-day practice

I can't imagine how wonderful you must feel for the work you've done in this journal. I hope you can look back and see the growth and change reflected in the pages. Take some time to solidify that growth and put your reflection into words.

In the space below, free-write about the last 90 days. How have you been impacted by this journal? How have you grown? What changes have occurred in your life because of this practice?

thank you!

Darling Soul, thank you so much for investing in this journal, and investing in yourself. I hope you found this experience insightful, meaningful, and encouraging. You deserve a beautiful, whole, and rich life. I invite you to continue investing in yourself and giving yourself the gift of healing. You deserve it.

notes

notes

notes

notes

notes

notes

notes

notes

notes

notes

notes

references

Baikie, K. (n.d.). Developmental Stages of the Child. Retrieved from http://www.karenbaikie.com.au/resources/HAA_News_Child_Development.pdf

A basic introduction to child development theories. (n.d.). Retrieved October 30, 2020, from https://mhs.mcsd.org/UserFiles/Servers/Server_21163/File/Library%20Media%20Center/theories_outline.pdf

Bradshaw, J. (1990). Homecoming: Reclaiming and championing your inner child. London: Piatkus.

Dale, C. (2020). Energy healing for trauma, stress & chronic illness: Uncover & transform the subtle energies that are causing your greatest hardships. Woodbury, MN: Llewellyn Publications. Heller, D. P. (2019). The power of attachment: How to create deep and lasting intimate relationships. Boulder, CO: Sounds True.

Kolk, B. V. (2015). The Body Keeps the Score. Penguin. Shaffer, D. R., & Kipp, K. (2007). Developmental psychology: Childhood and adolescence. Belmont, CA: Wadsworth/Thomson. Wolynn, M. (2017). It didn't start with you: How inherited family trauma shapes who we are and how to end the cycle. New York, NY: Penguin Books.

Wong, D. W., Hall, K. R., & Hernandez, L. W. (2021). Counseling individuals through the lifespan. Los Angeles, CA: SAGE.

copyright notice

Disclaimer: I am not, nor do I claim to be a medical professional.

If you are having suicidal thoughts, please use these resources:

National Suicide Hotline: 1-800-273-8255
Crisis Textline: text "HOME" to 741741

Made in the USA
Las Vegas, NV
06 September 2021

29663136R00086